This number book belongs to:

Colour the **tallest** house green.

Colour the flower in **front** of Elephant red.

Colour the banana **under** Monkey yellow.

Draw a small bird at the **top** of the tree.

Number hunt!

Elephant has invited his friends over to play.
Can you read all the numbers you see?

1 2 3 4 5 6 7 8 9 10 ☆ 1 2 3 4

Sort and count the toys. Write the numbers in the boxes.

How many cars? ☐   How many balls? ☐

How many blocks? ☐   How many telephones? ☐

Sorting and counting

Go on a number hunt in your own house, looking for numbers and things to sort and count. Discuss with your child what the numbers are used for. Ask, for example: 'What do the numbers on the clock tell us?'

Sort and count

Monkey is tidying up her toys. Count how many are in each set. Draw a line to the correct number.

Counting

Help your child to sort and count his own toys. The more practice he gets counting real objects the better.

Tiger isn't sure how many cars she has. Count how many there are of each colour. Write the numbers in the boxes.

☐ green cars

☐ blue cars

☐ red cars

☐ brown cars

☐ purple cars

Does Tiger have more green cars or more red cars?

Counting

Encourage your child to count these groups of cars in a systematic way, each time starting with the car in the top left-hand corner, so that he doesn't miss any.

How many?

Count how many hats Snake is wearing in each picture and write the number in the box.

☐ hats   ☐ hats   ☐ hats

How many hats is Snake wearing here?

None!

Now *you* draw the right number of hats on Snake to match the numbers.

2 hats   0 hats   5 hats

Zero

Understanding the idea of nothing in number is a basic skill. Play vanishing tricks and then make objects reappear. Nothing can also be called zero or nought.

For this page you need one die . Throw it to see what number you get. Put a ring round the set with that number of fruit in it. Keep going until you've put a ring round each set.

Bananas are my favourite!

Yum! Yum!

Sorting

Invent sorting and collecting activities using dice. For example: 'Throw the die and find the same number of blocks.'

Sort the shapes

Monkey is looking for triangles. She knows that they have three corners and three straight sides.

Draw a ring round all the triangles.

My hat is a triangle!

Sorting shapes

Go on a shape hunt in your home or while out on walks. How many triangles, for example, can your child find?

8

Help Tiger and Elephant to sort these shapes.

Squares have four corners and four straight sides, all the same length.

Rectangles have two long sides and two short sides. They have four corners.

Colour the **circles** blue.

Colour the **squares** red.

Colour the **rectangles** green.

What shapes haven't you coloured?

Sorting shapes

Talk to your child about the differences between shapes.

Snake has made a pattern using three different colours but only one circle shape.

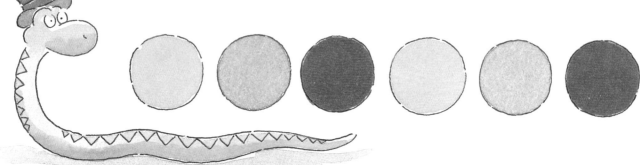

Colour these circles to match Snake's pattern.

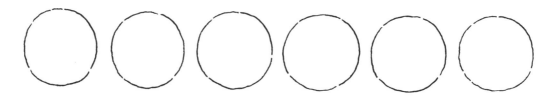

Now choose another shape and see if you can make your own pattern using different colours.

Sequencing

Set out simple patterns for your child to copy using blocks or buttons. Start by using one or two shapes or colours. This will give him plenty of practical experience. You can even ask him to set out patterns for you to copy, too!

Tiger has made a pattern using different shapes, but only one colour. It is red.

Can you copy Tiger's pattern here?

Monkey's pattern has different shapes *and* colours.

Can you copy it here?

Sequencing
Being able to recognise patterns is an important part of mathematics. If your child can see patterns in shapes and the way they are set out, it will help him to recognise them in numbers.

Shape picture

○ Colour the circles yellow. ⬭ Colour the ovals blue.

△ Colour the triangles green. ♥ Colour the hearts pink.

■ Colour the squares red. ◇ Leave the diamonds white.

▬ Colour the rectangles brown.

Sorting shapes

Talk to your child about the picture. For example say: 'How many triangles can you see? Which triangle is the biggest? Can you see any triangles that are the same size?'

Talk and point

Match the object to its label.

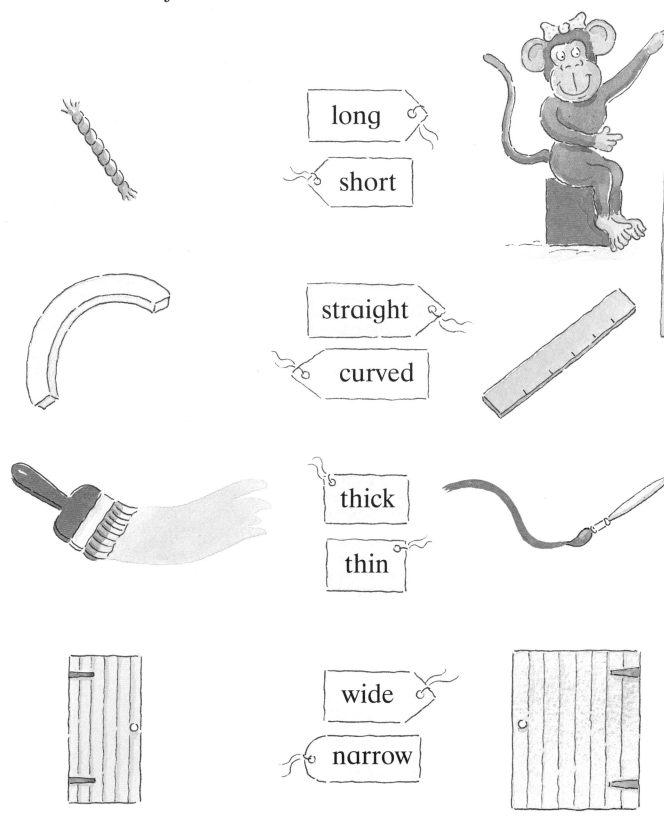

long

short

straight

curved

thick

thin

wide

narrow

Comparisons

Play the talk and point opposites game at home. Can your child point to the big cup/the small cup, the bottom shelf/the top shelf, etc?

13

The animal race

Which animal has come first in the race?
Which animal is second?
Which animal is last?

Draw a crown on who came first.
Draw a cap on who came second.
Draw a bow on who came third.

Ordinal numbers
The numbers first, second, third, etc are called ordinal numbers.

Leaf prints

The animals have made lots of leaf prints. Draw a line to match the print with the correct leaf.

Matching prints

Your child could make his own paint prints. Try leaves, sponges, hands or feet! Another fun activity is making rubbings of coins. Can he match the rubbings to the correct coins?

Spot the difference

Draw a circle round the one that **isn't** the same as the others. Look really hard!

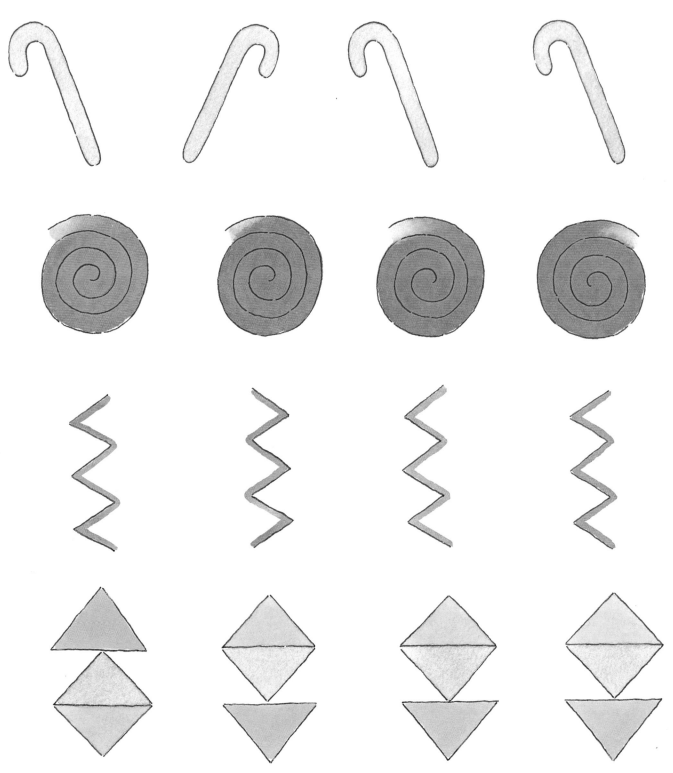

Looking for differences

Your child will need to look closely to detect the differences. This will help him to develop better observation skills.

Tiger needs help with her jigsaw puzzle. Draw a line to show which pieces go together.

Looking for differences

Jigsaw puzzles are a great way to help your child to notice differences. You could make your own jigsaw by gluing pictures onto card and then cutting them up.

Same both sides

These things are exactly the same shape on the left side as on the right side. They are **symmetrical**.

Half of each shape is missing. Finish them carefully so that they are symmetrical.

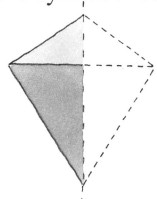

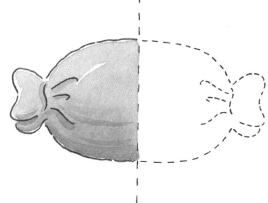

The right half of Monkey's face is missing! Can you draw it, exactly the same as the left?

Symmetry

Go on a hunt for things that are symmetrical in your house. You can test for symmetry by drawing an imaginary or real line down the centre of the object.

Monkey has lots of toys. Colour any toys that are symmetrical in shape.

Help your child to make great symmetry paint patterns by painting half the page and then folding it over. Open up for a lovely surprise!

Measuring

Use some of your building blocks or squares of paper to measure Snake. Count how many blocks you've used.

How many blocks long is Snake? □

How many blocks tall is Monkey's tree? □

How many blocks long is Elephant's trunk? □

Make sure all your blocks are the same size.

Measuring

Encourage your child to explore and experiment before showing him how to line up the blocks on top of the item to be measured. The measurement doesn't need to be exact, but try to encourage your child to close up any gaps between blocks.

Place your hand in the space below.
Trace round it with a pencil and colour it.
This is called your hand span.

How many blocks wide is your hand?

How many hand spans long is your bed?

How many hand spans high
is your favourite chair?

One, two,
three...

Measuring

You could help your child to trace his hand span on a piece of scrap paper, then cut it out. He can then use it for measuring and counting things.

In the kitchen

Whose cup has the most juice? Colour their juice orange.

Colour the empty cup below with your favourite coloured juice.

Have you given yourself **more** or **less** juice than Elephant has?

Measuring

Let your child help you to measure ingredients when you are cooking. This will help him to see how useful numbers are to us.

Help the animals to finish decorating the cake. They will tell you what to do.

Draw a triangle in the centre of the cake, below the squares.

Join the dots together to make a curved line.

Draw five more circles round the edge at the top of the cake, to make some curls.

What have you made? Colour the picture.

Following instructions

Have fun following and giving instructions. This will help your child to become more confident with using mathematical language.

Sharing things equally

What a delicious pie. Let's cut it in half to make it fair.

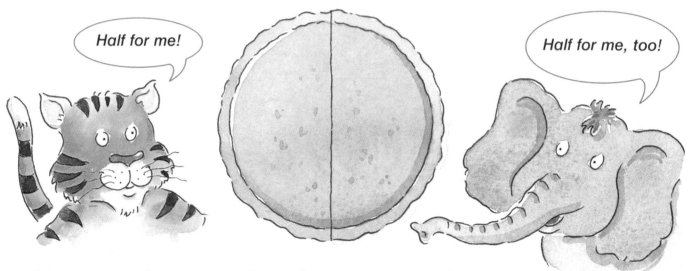

But now there are four hungry mouths to feed. Let's try again.

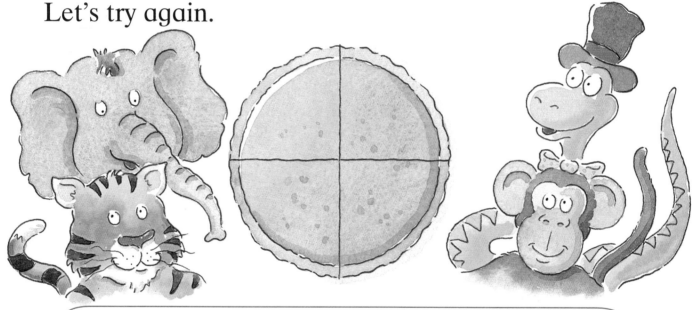

Halves and quarters

Food provides lots of practical opportunities for talking about halves and quarters.